Dear Parent:
Your child's love of reading starts here!

Every child learns to read in a different way and at his or her own speed. You can help your young reader improve and become more confident by encouraging his or her own interests and abilities. You can also guide your child's spiritual development by reading stories with biblical values and Bible stories, like I Can Read! books published by Zonderkidz. From books your child reads with you to the first books he or she reads alone, there are I Can Read! books for every stage of reading:

SHARED READING
Basic language, word repetition, and whimsical illustrations, ideal for sharing with your emergent reader.

BEGINNING READING
Short sentences, familiar words, and simple concepts for children eager to read on their own.

READING WITH HELP
Engaging stories, longer sentences, and language play for developing readers.

READING ALONE
Complex plots, challenging vocabulary, and high-interest topics for the independent reader.

ADVANCED READING
Short paragraphs, chapters, and exciting themes for the perfect bridge to chapter books.

I Can Read! books have introduced children to the joy of reading since 1957. Featuring award-winning authors and illustrators and a fabulous cast of beloved characters, I Can Read! books set the standard for beginning readers.

A lifetime of discovery begins with the magical words *"I Can Read!"*

Visit www.icanread.com for information on enriching your child's reading experience.
Visit www.zonderkidz.com for more Zonderkidz I Can Read! titles.

RUBY
Bakes a Cake

by Susan Hill
pictures by Margie Moore

A friend loves at all times.
—*Proverbs 17:17*

ZONDERKIDZ

Ruby Bakes a Cake

Copyright © 2004, 2010 by Susan Hill
Illustrations © 2004, 2010 by Margie Moore

Requests for information should be addressed to:
Zonderkidz, 3900 *Sparks Drive SE, Grand Rapids, Michigan 49546*

Library of Congress Cataloging-in-Publication Data
Long, Susan Hill
    Ruby bakes a cake / by Susan Hill ; [illustrations by Margie Moore].
       p.   cm. — (I can read book)
    Summary: Ruby Racoon asks her friends for advice on making a cake.
    ISBN 978-0-310-72022-5 (softcover)
    [1. Cake—Fiction. 2. Friendship—Fiction. 3. Raccoon—Fiction. 4. Animals—
Fiction.] I. Moore, Margie, ill. II. Title.
    PZ7.L8582Rue 2010
    [E]—dc22   2009033134

All Scripture quotations unless otherwise noted are taken from the *Holy Bible,
New International Reader's Version®*. NIrV®. Copyright © 1995, 1996, 1998 by
International Bible Society. Used by permission of Zondervan. All rights reserved.

Any Internet addresses (websites, blogs, etc.) and telephone numbers printed
in this book are offered as a resource. They are not intended in any way to be or
imply an endorsement by Zondervan, nor does Zondervan vouch for the content
of these sites and numbers for the life of this book.

Zonderkidz is a trademark of Zondervan.

Editor: Mary Hassinger

Printed in China

18 19 20 21 22 23 24 25 26 27 28 DSC 13 12 11 10 9 8 7 6 5 4 3

4

For Molly
—S. H.

For Jessie
—M. M.

Ruby Raccoon wanted

to bake a cake,

but she didn't know how.

"I will ask my friends

what it takes

to bake a cake," she said.

Ruby ran to the stone wall.

She saw Sam Squirrel.

"Sam, what does it take

to bake a cake?"

"Try adding nuts," said Sam.

"Thank you!" said Ruby.

"Come join me

when my cake is done!"

Ruby ran to the fence.

She saw Bunny Rabbit.

"Bunny, what does it take

to bake a cake?"

"Every cake needs carrot tops,"

said Bunny.

"Thank you!" called Ruby.

"Please come over

when my cake is done!"

Ruby ran to the brook.

She saw Dan Duck.

"Dan, what does it take

to bake a cake?"

"I have never made a cake,

but I always enjoy snails," said Dan.

"Thank you!" said Ruby.

"Please come to my house

when my cake is done!"

Ruby ran to the tree.

She saw Jenny Wren.

"Jenny, what does it take

to bake a cake?"

"Don't forget wiggly worms,"

said Jenny.

"Thank you very much!"

called Ruby.

"Please come over

when my cake is done!"

Ruby ran to the pond.

She saw Frankie Frog.

"Frankie, what does it take
to bake a cake?"

Flick. Flick. "Flies," said Frankie.

"Really?" said Ruby.

"Well, please join me

when my cake is done!"

Ruby ran home.

She put everything into a big bowl.

She mixed the batter up
and put it in a pan.

She baked it in the oven.

"This does not smell good,"

said Ruby.

Ruby's friends came to share her cake.

She took it out of the oven.

"This does not look good,"

said Ruby.

Ruby cut the cake.

She gave it to her friends.

Her friends began to eat.

"This does not taste good,"
said Ruby.

"No, no, Ruby,
the cake is nice and crunchy,"
said Sam.

24

"And the cake is good and tall,"
said Bunny.

"It has a lovely round shape,"
said Dan.

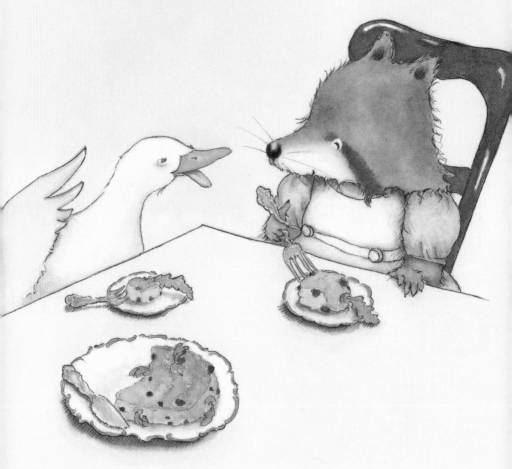

"I have never tasted
such a juicy cake,"
said Jenny.

"And what a color, Ruby!"

said Frankie.

"This is one green cake."

Ruby smiled.

"It is not a good cake," she said.

"But you are very good friends."